Fountain of Life

Fountain of Life

music for contemplative worship

Margaret Rizza

We hope you enjoy the music in this book. Further copies are available from your local music shop or Christian bookshop.

In case of difficulty, please contact the publisher direct by writing to:

The Sales Department
KEVIN MAYHEW LTD
Rattlesden
Bury St Edmunds
Suffolk IP30 0SZ

Phone 01449 737978   Fax 01449 737834

Please ask for our complete catalogue of outstanding Church Music.

Fountain of Life is available as follows:

1400147   **Full score** includes the complete vocal and instrumental parts
1450090   **Vocal score** includes the melody, keyboard, guitar and optional vocal parts
1480040   **Cassette** includes all twelve pieces directed by Margaret Rizza
1490024   **CD** includes all twelve pieces directed by Margaret Rizza

First published in Great Britain in 1997 by Kevin Mayhew Ltd.

© Copyright 1997 Kevin Mayhew Ltd.

ISBN 1 84003 061 5
ISMN M 57004 135 0
Catalogue No: 1400148

0 1 2 3 4 5 6 7 8 9

Front Cover: *Waterspray.*
Reproduced by courtesy of Images Colour Library Limited, London.
Cover design by Jaquetta Sergeant.

Music Editors: Adrian Vernon Fish and Donald Thomson
Music setting by Donald Thomson
Printed and bound in Great Britain

Contents

Foreword

My heart is ready, O God;
I will play and sing your praise.
Awake, my soul; awake lyre and harp.
I will awake the dawn.
O Lord, I will thank you among the peoples;
I will make music for you among the nations.

from Psalm 108

Fountain of Life was written as a response to a request to compose some music as an introduction to prayer.

Music allows us to enter a world of mystery and imagination. We leave behind our outer external lives which are so bound up with busyness, anxieties, intellectual concerns, plans and projects, to enter into the depths of our inner life. We share and respond to the creative force deep within our being – it is a journey towards 'the centre' to be touched and transformed by beauty and by love.

As we listen, music can perhaps break into our own personal, diverse and conflicting feelings which in turn can resonate with the pain, division and suffering in our world of which we are intrinsically a part. It can also bring us to heights of joy, freedom, gratitude, compassion, worship and praise.

Music can be part of our inner journey which brings us ultimately to the source of love within the ground of our being. It can free us and open up new creative responses which in turn flow out into our everyday life.

So how can music bring us into deeper prayer? In order for our lively minds to become quiet we need music of a meditative, contemplative nature. These very simple chants aim to help still our busy, distracted minds so that we are able to enter into a consciousness of simplicity where all variety, all complexity and multiplicity cease. It is a preparation to enter into the stillness and silence of prayer when we 'leave self behind' (Matthew 16:24-26) to become 'clay in the potter's hand' (Isaiah 64:8).

Each of the twelve pieces in *Fountain of Life* may be sung by one person alone, by two or three gathered together, by hundreds, or by a choir. They may be unaccompanied, accompanied by a single instrument or by a whole music group. They are infinitely expandable according to the resources of those involved. The instrumental variations are graded according to technical skill so there should be something for everyone.

My hope is that the music will be a preparation for prayer, leading to deeper prayer, both for those who sing and play it and for those who listen. I pray that it will bear much fruit.

MARGARET RIZZA

Singing these chants

All the melody lines in *Fountain of Life* are very easy to sing and should be possible for everyone with the exception of 'Come Lord' and 'Jesus, you are the way'. But even here, sing what you can and then when it goes too high just sing down the octave. Sing along, do whatever is comfortable and enjoy it!

About the composer

Margaret Rizza studied at the Royal College of Music, London, and the National School of Opera, London, and completed her operatic training in Siena and Rome. She has sung at many of the world's leading operatic venues, including La Scala, Milan, Glyndebourne, Sadler's Wells, and with the English Opera Group, and under such conductors as Benjamin Britten, Igor Stravinsky and Leonard Bernstein. She was also a frequent broadcaster.

Since 1977 she has taught singing and voice production at the Guildhall School of Music and Drama in London, and gives master-classes and workshops at summer schools. She also devotes much of her time to helping students to perform and share their music with the marginalised and with people with mental and physical disabilities. In recent years she has worked closely with music therapists.

She has trained and conducted several choirs, and is the founder of The Cameo Opera, The Cameo Singers and the St Thomas Music Group.

Since 1983 she has dedicated herself to the work of spirituality and to the wider aspect of music in the community. She has led many retreats, and is closely involved with the World Community for Christian Meditation (WCCM), as well as leading courses for prayer guides.

MAGNIFICAT

My soul praises and magnifies the Lord
Text: Luke 1: 46
Music: Margaret Rizza

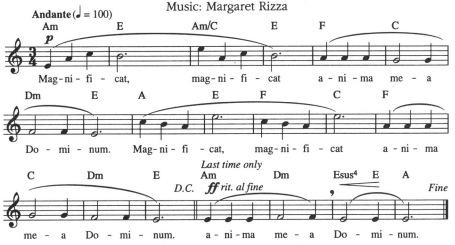

Mag-ni-fi-cat, mag-ni-fi-cat a-ni-ma me-a Do-mi-num. Mag-ni-fi-cat, mag-ni-fi-cat a-ni-ma me-a Do-mi-num. a-ni-ma me-a Do-mi-num.

VENI, LUMEN CORDIUM

Come, light of our hearts. Come, Holy Spirit, come
Text: Stephen Langton (d.1228)
Music: Margaret Rizza

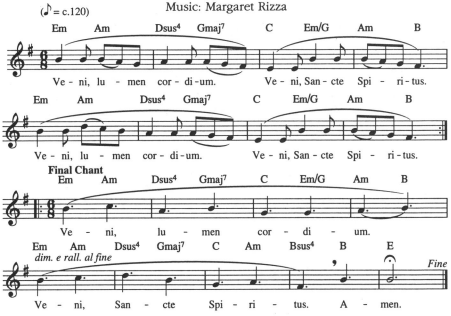

Ve-ni, lu-men cor-di-um. Ve-ni, Sanc-te Spi-ri-tus.

Final Chant

Ve-ni, lu-men cor-di-um. A-men.

YOU ARE THE CENTRE

Text and Music: Margaret Rizza

Pattern Guide

1. Introduction with C instrument to bar 20.
2. Sing verse 1.
3. C instrument variation to bar 20; voices tacet.
4. Sing verse 2.
5. Instrumental variation; voices hum to bar 20.

From bar 21 sing to the end using 2nd time bars.

2. You are the cen - tre, you are my life, you are the cen - tre, O Lord, of my life. Come, Lord, and heal me, Lord of my life, come, Lord, and teach me, Lord of my life. You are the cen - tre, Lord, of my life.

D.C.

COME TO ME

Text: Matthew 11: 28-30
Music: Margaret Rizza

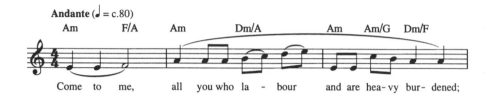

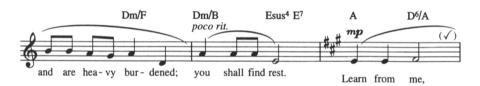

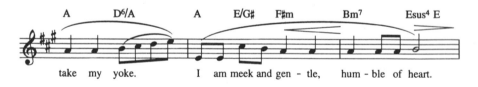

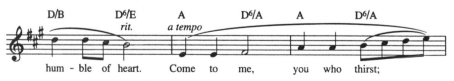

A   A/G♯   F♯m   Bm⁷   Esus⁴ E   A   F♯m/A

from my heart liv- ing wa- ters flow. Come to me,

D/G♯ C♯   F♯m F♯m/E D   Bm⁷   Esus⁴ E

you who thirst; from my heart liv- ing wa- ters flow.

D   E/D Amaj⁷/C♯   D   C♯/E♯   A⁷/E   Dmaj⁷ Bm/D

Come to me, you who thirst; from my heart

Bm⁷   Esus⁴ E⁷   A   D⁶/A   A   D⁶/A
poco rit.   *a tempo*

liv- ing wa- ters flow. Come to me, learn from me,

A   D⁶/A   A   D⁶/A   A   E⁷/A

come to me, learn from me, you shall find

A   E⁷/A   A   D⁶/A   A
dim. e rall.

rest, you shall find rest, you shall rest.

SEND FORTH YOUR SPIRIT

Text: Psalm 104
Music: Margaret Rizza

ADORAMUS TE, DOMINE DEUS

We adore you, O Lord God

Text: Unknown; Music: Margaret Rizza

SILENT, SURRENDERED

Text: v. 1: Pamela Hayes; v. 2: Margaret Rizza
Music: Margaret Rizza

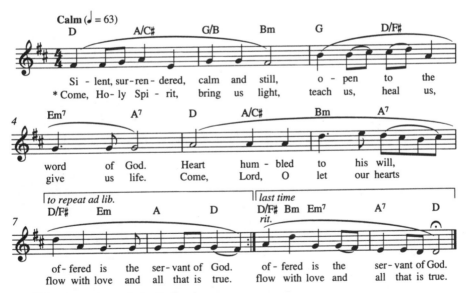

* Additional verse for use during Pentecost

COME, LORD

Text and Music: Margaret Rizza

come, Lord, give us your life, your life e - ter - nal, come, Lord,

come to your peo - ple, give us your last - ing peace.

Come, Lord, come, Lord, come, Lord, come, Lord.

JESUS, YOU ARE THE WAY

Text: Pamela Hayes
Music: Margaret Rizza

near. Je - sus, you are the way that I can see all the

Fa - ther means to me. Je - sus, you are the

way I can be - gin to let the Spi - rit breathe with - in.

Je - sus, my wea - ry head has found its rest in the beat - ing in your

breast. Je - sus, this a - lone can be my prayer,

you are the way, your pierced heart o - pen there.

Je - sus, you are the way, you are the way.

Je - sus, Je - sus, Je - sus,

you are the way.

19

O LORD, MY HEART IS NOT PROUD

Text: Psalm 131
Music: Margaret Rizza

FOUNTAIN OF LIFE

Text: Michael Forster
Music: Margaret Rizza

KYRIE, ELEISON

Text: Traditional
Music: Margaret Rizza

Lord, have mercy. Christ, have mercy. Lord, hear us.
Christ, have mercy. Lord, have mercy. Christ, hear us.